The ME
I came here to be

Written by Mona Chabra

Illustrated by Lana Lee

If I could I would...
Splash in puddles. And skip in the rain.

If I could I would...
Strap on a parachute and jump out of a plane.

If I could I would...
Hop on a surf board and ride a wave.

If I could I would...
Climb a mountain. And find a hidden cave.

If I could I would...
Skate on ice. And ski on snow.

If I could I would...
Ride a stallion in a rodeo.

If I could I would...
Dive deep into the bluest sea.

If I could I would...
Go to the forest and swing from a tree.

If I could I would...
Hit a home run. And steal a base.

If I could I would...
Compete in a track meet and win the race.

If I could I would...
Walk on the beach and make footprints in the sand.

If I could I would...
Play the tuba in a marching band.

But like fish don't use feet and dogs don't need wings.

I simply wasn't meant to do certain things.

We're all unique in our own special way.

1 Blessing   2 Blessings   3 Blessings

I count my blessings everyday.

And would just like to say.

I chose this journey so it's okay.

I'm not mad or a tiny bit sad.

Believe it or not I'm actually glad.

And think it's pretty sweet!

Because if I could I would never meet

The OMG version of me.

I came here to be!

Mona's Wish List for the World

♥ I wish people wouldn't say "Sorry" when they find out I have disabilities. I'm not sorry. My disabilities have made me the person I am!

♥ I wish people would take the time to talk to me face to face. My speech is unclear but if you're patient and put forth the effort to actually listen to what I have to say you will definitely understand!

♥ I wish people wouldn't say "She used to be normal". Yes, I walked and talked with no apparent limitations until the age of six. But I was born with a genetic condition that took its time to show its true colors. So, the "normal" I came here for is now!

♥ I wish people wouldn't see me as a disability. A disability doesn't define a person. It's only an attribute. Like I'm Indian American, female, intelligent and, of course, beautiful I also have a disability!

♥ I wish people wouldn't treat me like I'm stupid or don't understand. Most disabilities whether physical or mental have no impact on intelligence. In fact, many of us have huge IQ's!

♥ I wish people wouldn't use their loud voice when they talk to me. It's true, some disabilities affect hearing but many don't. SO, PLEASE STOP SHOUTING!

♥ I wish people wouldn't view wheelchairs with such negativity. My wheelchair gives me the power to travel the world so everyone can see I'll never let my limitations limit me!

♥ I wish people wouldn't be afraid to interact with me just because I have disabilities. Each of us came here in our own custom-made body to experience the life we chose to live. We may look different or function in different ways. But if you fill your eyes with love instead of fear you'll see we are all just the same!

Author **Mona Chabra**

I took my first plane ride seated in my mom's tummy on July 4, 1970 from Indore to Ohio where I was born two months later. As I began walking and running like most kids, my travels took me on ordinary car rides, bike rides, boat rides, bus rides, train rides, amusement park rides, pony rides and, even occasional, camel rides! But, I would soon discover the adventure I had come for would be far from ordinary.

A few months after my sixth birthday, I started walking with a limp which continued until I was ready to sit down in the chair with wheels for the ride of my life!

My wheelchair gave me the power and ability to:

- Travel to eight counties and fifteen US states
- Go away to college and live in a dorm
- Earn 4 college degrees
- Pursue a career in writing
- Get married and divorced
- Carry my baby to full-term and deliver him naturally

I'm thankful for my phenomenal family and friends as well as all the love and blessings in my life that helped me believe and know I COULD and WOULD!